Variable Frequency Drives
Installation & Troubleshooting

By

Gary D. Anderson

VARIABLE FREQUENCY DRIVES
INSTALLATION & TROUBLESHOOTING

Every effort has been made in preparation of this book to ensure accuracy in presenting the concepts, information and common usage of Variable Frequency Drives in typical industrial environments. However, the information contained herein is sold without any expressed or implied warranty.

First Published: June 2013
Variable Frequency Drives: Installation & Troubleshooting

ISBN: 978-1-7341898-7-2

Contents

CHAPTER 1: INTRODUCTION TO MOTOR CONTROL DESIGN

Motor & Control Systems:

Those of you familiar with modern industry and manufacturing know that there are many different reasons for controlling the speed of an electric motor. These driving factors usually center on the manufacturing process being used; as well as the need to conserve and use energy resources efficiently. So the principle advantage of speed control is to gain the capability for operating at less than full load capacity during those times when it's optimal to do so.

In most any industrial plant, variable frequency drives (VFDs), have become a common and cost effective method of providing speed control and soft-start capability in a wide array of production applications that use AC induction motors. Motor Control has many facets. To fully understand VFD control, it's helpful to have a good understanding of some of the traditional control methods used in the past. We take a look at some of these methods in the following section.

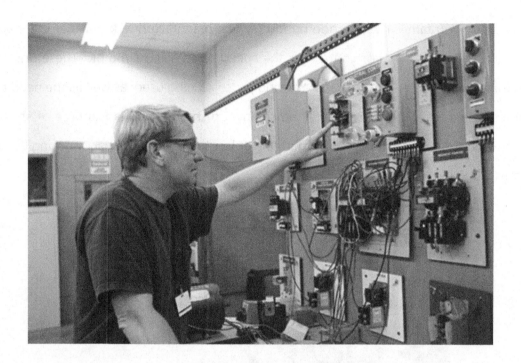

There are many things to consider when designing a system that will use a VFD for motor control. These things center on the application and what it will require to meet desired objectives. What are the loads that will be placed upon the motor and VFD? What will the load require from the system in terms of torque? Will torque requirements be constant or variable? What types of load will the motor/drive system be moving? This may be a conveyor system loaded with coal, a pump moving liquid, a fan moving air, or a process that requires precise positioning such as the axis movements of a CNC machining center. Will the installation be in a hazardous environment? What is the distance between the drive (VFD) and the motor? What type of braking will be satisfactory for the application? In addition to these considerations are the added factors of space requirements, cost of installation and maintenance, and the degree of control that must be maintained or monitored. Finally, decisions will be made pertaining to specific components, location for the VFD, and the wiring or cable requirements.

Why a VFD – A Lesson in Contrasts:

While a VFD may not be the answer for every application, I have found them extremely versatile in their applicability in many situations. With advances in solid-state electronics, VFDs stand in stark contrast with older, usually mechanical, methods of dealing with motor speed issues. Remember that older systems still required an electric motor running at its full speed.

In times past, mechanical measures would be taken to achieve a measure of speed control on the loads involved. This might be speed reduction gearing or sheaves, throttle-valves, types of magnetic or eddy-coupled devices or vane-pitch control on a turbine or fan. Since the motor continues to run at full-speed these partial-load methods prove wasteful in terms of energy consumption. VFDs are often used to replace these older, less efficient systems, thus reducing energy costs and gaining more precise control over motor speeds. However; it is commonplace to find many of these traditional types of electrical motor controls still being used in the industrial workplace. These control systems range from the traditional full-voltage, across-the-line motor contactors to many other different - and sometimes antiquated - *reduced-voltage* starting methods. Full-voltage starting, even though being economical to implement, creates greater demand on the electrical system by drawing up to 700% of the FLA of the motor rating during start-up. Also, for loads requiring a low speed / high torque startup, this method is unsuitable.

Other methods of reduced voltage starting would be a wye-delta control set-up, auto-transformer starters, or in some cases a partial-winding type AC induction motor. While providing reduced voltage and lower current start-up, none of these methods provide the capability to operate *continuously* at less than full-load. Below are various diagrams showing these basic motor control methods.

Primary Resistance Starter:

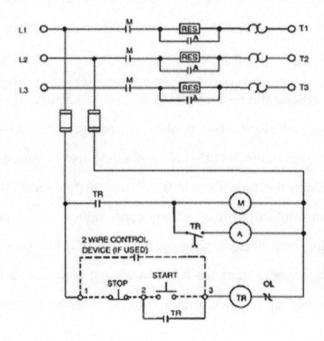

Autotransformer Starter:

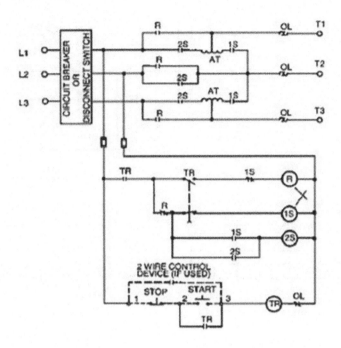

Part-Winding Motor & Starter:

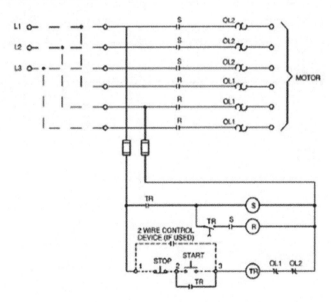

5

Wye-Delta Starter:

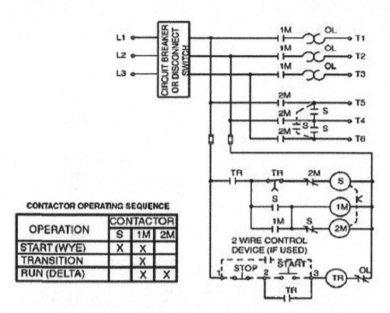

CONTACTOR OPERATING SEQUENCE

OPERATION	CONTACTOR		
	S	1M	2M
START (WYE)	X	X	
TRANSITION		X	
RUN (DELTA)		X	X

Soft-Start:

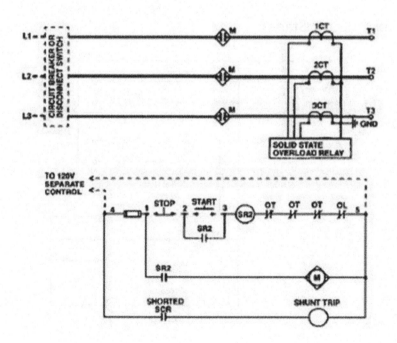

6

Note that these control systems, with the possible exception of the "soft-start", use some form of timer to cycle the elements used in providing reduced-voltage to the motor. When the applied voltage is reduced, the motor operates at a reduced speed, but also provides less torque. When the motor is operating at a reduced speed there is greater "slip" between stator (the rotating magnetic field) and the rotor of the motor. This increased slip equates to reduced efficiency. Also, when the driven loads still require full torque at reduced speeds these methods cannot be used.

These types of reduced voltage starting mechanisms are often used to run AC motors at slower speeds if the application only requires low torque values. However, in most of the above applications, once the timer has completed its function, the control system will apply full voltage and run the motor at its full-load/speed rating. This of course doesn't allow for periods of less than peak demand, where it would be advantageous to operate a motor and its load at less than the full-load rating of the motor.

The only way for an AC motor to maintain constant torque values through the full range of applied voltage is to apply a proportional reduction in the frequency of the applied voltage as well - the voltage to frequency ratio; (V/Hz), must be constant.

For a motor rated at 460 volts and 60 Hz, this ratio (460/60) would equate to *7.66*. Thus, in order to control the speed of an AC motor at the greatest efficiency, and yet provide constant torque needed for the applied load, it is necessary to vary both the voltage and the frequency of voltage supplied to the motor. This is exactly what is accomplished by using a VFD to power a motor. It can provide full torque to high inertia loads at lower voltage/current values, and run a continuous duty application at lower speeds if required. Here is a simple diagram of a VFD that details the various voltage forms throughout each section of the drive, from voltage input to the output going to the motor. Please note that this represents only the voltage changes from input to motor output, and not the complex signals that control the firing of IGBTs or other solid state components used to create the desired output voltage and frequency. These are aspects of the VFD that are microprocessor controlled, and thus are programmed – usually by parameter settings, when configuring the drive. However, I think this simple diagram is a good point in which to begin a study of how a VFD provides speed control for a motor.

Typical VFD Diagram:

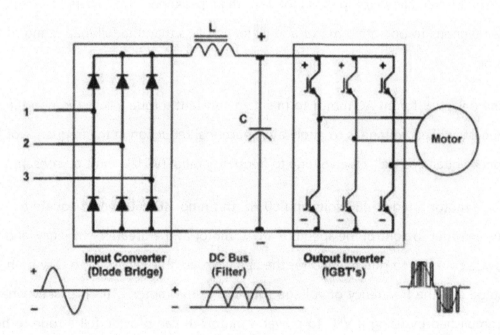

This diagram is a simple way of representing the changes occurring in the electrical current supplied to VFD and the motor. While this will be discussed in somewhat greater detail in the chapters that follow, for now we can summarize those changes as follows:

- *A VFD creates the output voltage and frequency to be supplied to the motor by rectifying the input AC into a DC voltage, then using pulse-width modulation (PWM) to recreate an AC current waveform.*

This output waveform is determined by microprocessor controlled firing of IGBTs in the output inverter section of the drive. Remember that the benefit to be gained by using a VFD is that it can cause the motor to run at full torque through the full speed range of the motor. It accomplishes this in the output inverter section, by keeping the voltage to frequency ratio (V/Hz) at a constant throughout the speed range of the motor. Note that this is the normal (rated) speed range of the motor. There may be other instances where a motor would be driven at a higher speed than it normal rating; for instance at 80 or 90 Hz. As you will see in the section that follows, as speeds (RPM) increased beyond the rated speed of the motor, the torque supplied by the motor dramatically decreases. As shown in the sections that follow, it all depends on the types of loads being driven.

Some loads require the same amount torque whether the motor is running at a low speed or at the full rated speed of the motor. This is referred to as a *constant torque* application and essentially follows the simple diagram as shown. Regardless of motor RPM, the loading on the motor is approximately the same.

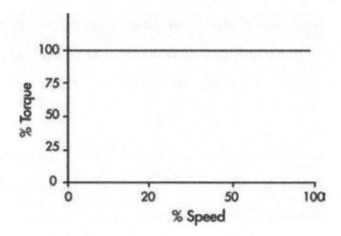

In other types of loads, the required torque may significantly drop as the speed of the motor increases, so the highest torque required by the load is at the lower motor RPM. In this instance the VFD is operating in a *constant horsepower (HP) mode.*

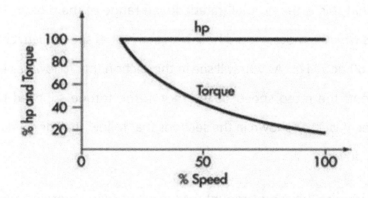

Note that this diagram represents a *type of load* where the torque necessary to handle a load begins to fall-off once the motor is at approximately 25% of its rated speed. As mentioned, this also happens once a motor exceeds 100% of its rated speed, but the drop in torque is more linear.

CHAPTER 2: ELECTRICAL & MOTION FUNDAMENTALS

Now that we have covered some of the basic ideas involved with speed control, let's briefly mention some topics that may further clarify these concepts.

Physical Properties: Torque, Speed & Horsepower:

- *Synchronous Speed*: The speed of the rotating electrical field in the stator windings of an electric motor. The formula for synchronous speed is:

$$RPM_{sync} = \frac{120\ f_{(Hz)}}{number\ of\ poles}$$

- *Slip:* The amount, usually presented on the motor nameplate as a percentage, which represents the ratio difference between the rotor speed (motor shaft) and the "synchronous" speed of the motor. Slip will vary with the load placed upon the motor.

$$Slip = \frac{n_{sync} - n_{rotor}}{n_{sync}}$$

- *Actual motor speed*: The synchronous speed of the motor less *slip.* This is what will be listed on the motor nameplate.

- *Power:* The rate of doing work – a measurement of work done over a specific time period. The common units for describing power are "horsepower" (HP) and watts. Motors produced in the U.S. are usually marked with a HP rating on the motor nameplate, while motors produced in European countries, such as Siemens or Fanuc, are usually rated with a KW (kilowatt) rating. One HP is equal to 550 lb-ft per second. That is the amount of power needed to lift 550 pounds one foot high in one second of time. More relevant to our discussion however, is the way in which power and torque are related. Note that the HP or KW listed on a motor nameplate is a full load / full speed rating. Here, by putting it into algebraic terms and shown in the diagrams that follow, we see that HP for a motor is determined by values of Torque and RPM.

HP = Torque x RPM (speed)

Torque = HP / RPM

Torque = force x radius

- *Torque:* It would be difficult to understand AC induction motors without at least a basic understanding of torque. Torque is the instantaneous vector force placed upon a radius, such as a motor shaft. It is basically *rotational force* and is defined in the same terms as work and energy (lb-ft), or foot-pounds. Torque can be expressed as the following formula: *torque = force x radius*. As with any force, the *torque the motor provides <u>must be greater</u> than the opposing load torque for any work to occur.*

Types of Motor Torque:

There are four types of torque commonly related to electric motors and their ability to move a designated load. Note that the following examples are for AC induction motors. When looking at AC Servomotors, such as would be used for CNC axis positioning, the torque and speed relationships are quite different. Here is a familiar Torque and Speed diagram that is typical for most induction motors. Obviously, for a motor to produce any work, it must be capable of producing enough torque, either on its own or through a gearbox, to overcome the connected load torque and inertia.

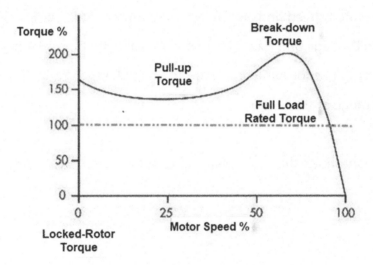

Here are several terms pertaining to the basic concept of torque as a motor accelerates toward its full-speed RPM value.

- *Locked Rotor Torque*: The produced torque as full-power is applied to a motor when the shaft is stationary (zero speed).

13

- *Pull-up Torque:* The produced torque as the motor accelerates to near its full rated speed.

- *Break-down Torque:* Basically the maximum torque a motor can produce at full rated speed. At this point the rotor speed is nearly equal to the synchronous speed in the windings of the stator. Beyond this speed, the torque of the motor rapidly falls off and can create a stalled motor condition.

- *Full-Load Torque:* The torque produced when a motor operates at its fully rated speed. Remember the concept of the *V/Hz* ratio. If the motor is operating at its fully rated speed and also at "full-load torque", it is because it is operating at its full voltage *and* Hz ratio. This is the value that must be held constant at all lower RPM's for full-load torque to be applied to the load throughout the speed range of the motor.

This diagram shows the basic relationship between Torque, HP, and Frequency:

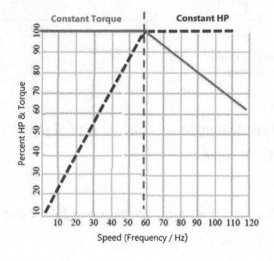

14

Motor RPM at approximately 60 Hz frequency, is the speed at which the motor can deliver both constant torque and function very near its fully rated HP. Beyond this frequency level, often referred to as *base speed*, the ability of a motor to provide torque starts to fall off dramatically.

Permanent Magnet / Servomotors:

Servomotors represent a much different class of motors than the traditional AC induction motor. This is mainly a result of different design characteristics, such as the use of permanent magnets embedded into the rotor, high density stator windings, and integrated feedback devices. Also different are the types of applications where they are used, predominately in CNC precision positioning applications. Basically, a permanent magnet servo motor is a *synchronous* motor that provides feedback for commutation, velocity, and positioning. In addition to this, they typically have a 30% to 60% higher torque capacity, faster acceleration and deceleration, and so provide significant torque over a wide speed range. They are generally characterized by a compact design, and provide high power density, low inertia, and higher efficiency than an AC induction motor. Typically, they are matched with servo drives from the same manufacturer.

Much like AC induction motors and the applications already discussed; the VFD drives used with servomotors also utilize microprocessor control, feedback, and programming to provide a PWM current for servomotor output. Because of this, many of the testing procedures used in troubleshooting these drives are the same. Here is a diagram representing the typical Speed/Torque curve for permanent magnet servomotors.

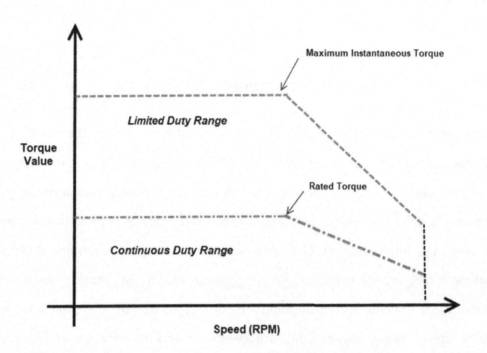

As evident from this diagram, servomotors can produce a torque well beyond their continuous duty rating for short periods of time, and generally at substantially greater speeds. For instance, where the torque curve starts its downward movement, might very well be at approximately 3500 to 3000 RPM range. So again; servomotors are characterized by significant torque over a wide speed range, which makes them ideal for CNC and robotic positioning applications.

Types of Motor Loads:

To best determine how to control a motor; whether it's an AC induction motor or permanent magnet servomotor, it is necessary to carefully consider the *type of load* that will be placed upon it. Listed below are the four common load types and common applications for each.

Constant Torque Load:

This type of load requires that the torque produced by the motor be constant throughout the full speed range of the motor. The load torque which the VFD and motor must overcome stays at an approximate constant force - regardless of motor speed. Load Torque remains a constant, regardless of motor speed. Beyond the base speed of the motor, as mentioned earlier, the torque which the motor is able to provide will begin to drop.

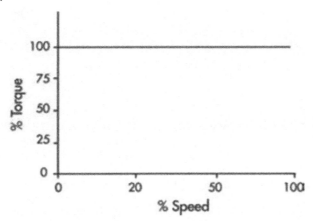

At higher than rated speed, frequency increases to the speed of the motor, without the corresponding increase in voltage to motor windings, create a stall situation with the motor and load. Increases in speed also *increases the horsepower* produced up to the full-speed rating of the motor.

Constant Horsepower Load:

   This type of load allows for the torque produced by a motor to *decrease* as the motor speed increases. The highest torque required by the application occurs during startup and at lower motor speeds.

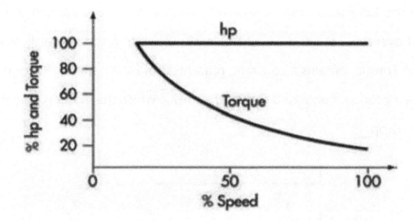

   As motor speed increased the V/Hz ratio is not required to be kept constant and torque provided by the motor is allowed to fall-off, even as horsepower remains constant throughout the speed range of the motor.

Variable Torque Load:

This is a type of load where the torque required from the motor increases as its speed increases. The torque load placed upon the motor and drive is lower when running at lower motor speeds. This is characteristic of centrifugal pumps, or centrifugal and axial fans, where increased motor RPM also increases the volume of fluid or air being moved.

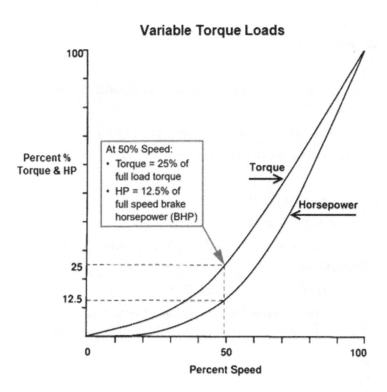

Thus, for these types of loads, torque (t) increases with the square of the speed and horsepower increases with the cube of the speed. Over-current faults may be a recurring problem at higher RPM because of increased loading on the motor.

Summary on Types of Loads:

1. <u>Variable Torque Load</u>
    a. Typical Applications:
        i. Centrifugal fans, centrifugal pumps, blowers and HVAC systems.
    b. Characteristics:
        i. HP varies as the cube of the speed.
        ii. Torque varies as the square of the speed

2. <u>Constant Torque Load</u>:
    a. Typical Applications:
        i. Mixers, Conveyors, Compressors and Hoists.
    b. Characteristics:
        i. Torque remains the same at all speeds.
        ii. HP varies directly with the speed.

3. <u>Constant Horsepower Load</u>:
    a. Typical Applications:
        i. Machine Tools, Lathes, Milling machines, Punch Presses
    b. Characteristics:
        i. Develops the same HP at all speeds.
        ii. Torque varies inversely with the speed.

4. <u>Impact Loads</u>:
    a. Typical Applications:
        i. Rock or coal crushers, general high inertia loads
        ii. Characteristics: Wide range of operational loading from light to several hundred percent of the motor rating.

CHAPTER 3: ELECTRICAL & POWER PRINCIPLES

Listed here are some common terms and equations that are helpful for understanding electricity in general; as well as induction motors and VFD control. A good understanding of these concepts will help you whenever you need to troubleshoot existing drive applications.

- Ohm's Law: **$E=IR$**, where:
  - E=voltage (EMF)
  - I = amperage (Electron flow or current)
  - R *or* Z = Ohms (Resistance or Impedance to current flow)
- Power (watts) = volts x amps
- 1 HP = 735 W or 0.7354 kW
- PF(*power factor*) = True Power (Watts) / Apparent Power (va)

The *Ohm's Law equation* shows how voltage, current and impedance are related in an electrical circuit; while the *Power equation* shows the basic relationship between power measured in wattage, voltage and amperage.

Note that for AC voltages, *power factor* is considered in electrical motor calculations. It is usually expressed as a decimal number or percentage, and is the ratio of *true power* (wattage) to *apparent power*. *True power* and *apparent power* are approximately equal if the load on the circuit is purely resistive. In an inductive circuit, such as a 3-phase induction motor, the current will lag the voltage sinewave resulting in a lower wattage value. Therefore with inductive loads, PF will normally be less than 1. For AC induction motors, PF of 0.80 to 0.90 is typical.

- **Voltage (E):**

The measure of electrical force in the circuit. Conceptually similar to a fluid based system where there must be greater pressure at one point for flow to occur to another point, so too must there be a differential voltage between points for current flow to occur.

- **Current (I):**

The flow or transfer of electrons through a conductor or circuit, and measured in amperage or Amps.

- **Resistance (R) or Impedance (Z):**

Resistance can be defined as the opposition of a conductor or circuit, to oppose or impede the flow of current. The unit of measurement is the Ohm. Impedance is applicative to AC (alternating current), and takes into account factors of inductive and capacitive reactance that occur in circuits that utilize alternating current.

When considering impedance or (Z) values it is important to note that it is derived from the resistive load on a circuit and also the inductive and capacitive loads. These last two types of loads present oppositions to current flow in a AC circuit called *inductive reactance* (X_L) and *capacitive reactance* (X_C), both of which are caused by the collapsing magnetic fields intrinsic to AC voltage. Therefore the equation for impedance in a given circuit is as follows and takes into account the total resistance to current flow.

$$Z_{(Ohms)} = R + X_L + X_C$$

- **Power (W or kW):**

Power, measured in kilowatts (kW) or watt (W), is directly related to the calculations for torque that a motor can supply to a load. Recall the equations:

$$P = E \times I$$

$$Torque = HP / RPM$$

$$1\ HP = 735\ W$$

It also is used in calculating power factor (PF), which is used in motor calculations involving AC power.

Waveform Characteristics:

- **Sine Wave**:

Electrical power in which the values of voltage and current change over a specific time period. This is due to how this type of electrical current is produced – one cycle or wave being one full rotation or 360° of the generator rotor. This is the common way to diagram the voltage and current of alternating current, and shows both the positive and negative alternations of current flow.

Sine-wave

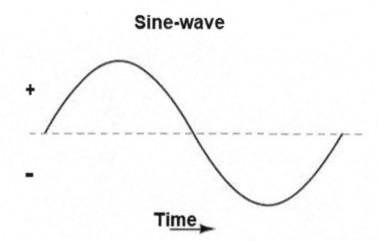

- **Frequency**:

This is the number of times a sine-wave repeats during one second of time. The unit of measurement for frequency is the hertz (Hz). It is often convenient to calculate the time period for a single cycle, which of course would be the reciprocal of the frequency. Therefore for a frequency of 60 Hz, the *period* would be 1/60 or .0166 seconds.

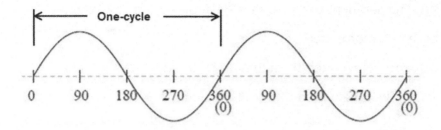

Frequency (Hz) = Number of Cycles per Second

- **Square Wave:**

A waveform that rises to specific amplitude, but in which the transition time is very negligible. Basically transitioning from 0 volts to its full voltage in a time period or "rise time" that is zero. Like the sine-wave, the square-wave utilized on variable frequency drives, has both positive and negative alternations.

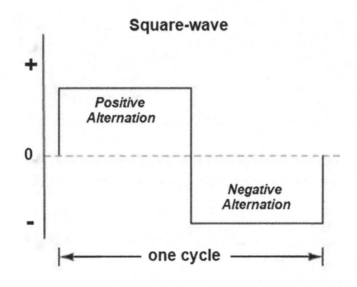

The square wave is used to create VFD output by utilizing the concept of *pulse width modulation.* The pertinent concepts that are applicable for creating the desired output current for the AC motor are:

- *Frequency:* How often the alternation turned to an "on" state.
- *Width*: The time period of the alternation.

- **Amplitude:**

The voltage or current presented by a sine-wave during any instantaneous point in time. Various calculations can be made using the amplitude of a voltage sine wave once its peak voltage (PV) is measured. These measurements would include the peak-to-peak voltage (PPV), Root Mean Square voltage (RMS), and Average Voltage values.

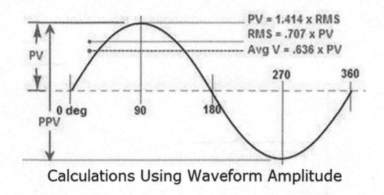

Calculations Using Waveform Amplitude

RMS voltage is the mathematical average of the sums of all voltage levels of an AC sine-wave. Therefore; the common household voltage of 120 volts, such as in a living room receptacle outlet, is derived from a sine-wave of approximately 170 PV.

CHAPTER 4: VARIABLE FREQUENCY DRIVE FUNDAMENTALS:

Typical VFD Diagram:

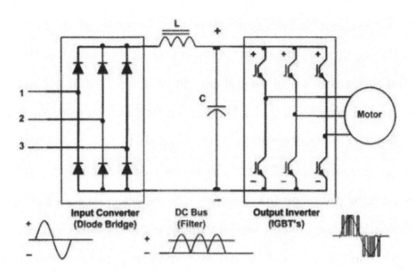

Here again is the basic diagram for a variable frequency drive using *Pulse Width Modulation* (PWM), to provide the desired output current. While there are other types of adjustable speed drives, such as the current source inverter (CSI), and the variable voltage inverter (VVI), the focus of this text is the PWM type which has become an industry standard due to its reliability. The PWM uses *insulated gate bipolar transistors,* or IGBTs, in the inverter section of the drive. These are controlled by a microprocessor on the control board of the VFD, and provide very fast switching times.

Notice how the circuit shows three distinct sections. The first section shows the rectifier or *converter* portion of the drive, where a three-phase diode bridge rectifier changes the incoming AC voltage to a pulsating DC voltage. The middle section is the DC bus portion where the pulsating DC produced by rectification is filtered by the use

27

of capacitors to provide a smoothed DC voltage. The third section is the *transistor switching* or *inverter* section which produces, by the use of the IGBTs mentioned earlier, a three-phase AC current at the desired frequency and voltage amplitude.

In the first section (rectifier) you can see six diodes connected in a bridge circuit that will convert the input three phase AC voltage to a DC bus voltage. The filtered DC section of the circuit consists of several capacitors connected in parallel, and a large inductor connected in series with the DC bus. These capacitors charge and discharge in synchronization with the alternating input voltage which causes the half-wave signal to be converted to a smoothed DC voltage, as denoted by the positive (+) straight line running through the pulses on the diagram. The inductor, labeled by the "L" symbol, is used to filter and correct for current fluctuations in the resulting voltage. The voltage level at this point in the drive will be at approximately 1.414 times the input voltages. Thus for a 480 VAC input, the DC bus section would be at approximately 678 VDC. The capacitors will charge to the approximate peak voltage of the incoming voltage waveform with little voltage drop through the diode bridge.

In the inverter section of the VFD, you can see that the IGBTs connecting to each output phase are supplied by the DC bus. These IGBTs are switched to "on" and "off" states by a firing circuit controlled by the microprocessor located within the VFD. At the correct time each transistor is turned on, which then supplies a voltage pulse to the output of the drive and the AC motor. The following example shows the resulting waveform that is applied to each motor lead or phase. The action of the inverter section takes the DC bus voltage, and using Pulse Width Modulation (PWM) sends an applied voltage to the motor which appears as AC current. *Both the voltage amplitude of this hybrid output and its frequency, are functions of the length of time the voltage pulse is turned on and the time between pulses.*

Pulse Width Modulation:

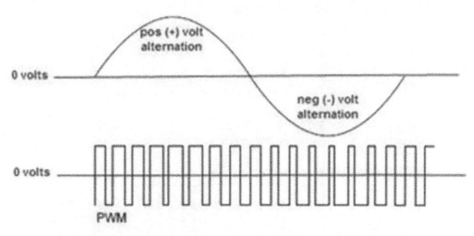

PWM to motor output approximates a sine-wave

In other words, the motor sees the applied voltage, created by microprocessor controlled pulsing of the filtered DC voltage in precise time sequencing, as a sine wave. The longer the pulse is "on" – the higher the resulting voltage output. Please recall that an AC voltage is the average of the peak voltages of each alternating half-cycle. You can see from the above diagram that the pulses that have the longer "on-time" coincide with the *higher amplitude* in the resulting sine wave.

Here is another example of PWM, where the positive and negative alternations can be illustrated more clearly. Also note, that not only is the voltage amplitude adjusted by the controlled firing of the IGBT's, the output frequency of the resultant sine wave is controlled and adjusted as well.

Example of Pulse Width Modulation

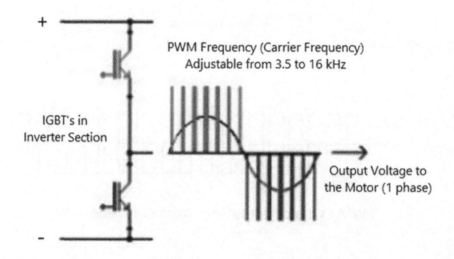

The output frequency is adjustable from 0 to 60 Hz with the *V/Hz ratio* remaining constant. In other words, for every decrease in frequency the drive will also lower the output voltage. This holds for frequency selections up to 60 Hz. Above this frequency value, the output voltages can go no higher, even though frequency is increasing, and the motor will lose efficiency. The following diagram visually depicts how both torque and HP are related to frequency.

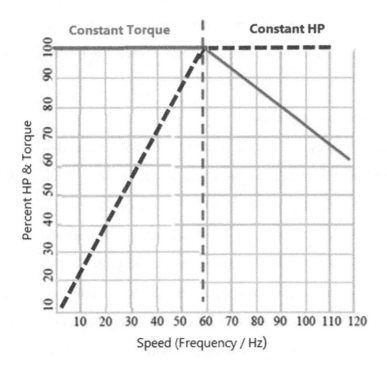

- **Carrier Frequency:**

Carrier frequency, often referred to as "**switching frequency**" is the term used to denote the frequency of the square-wave pulses produced by the inverter section of the drive. The firings of the transistors are determined by the microprocessor and can usually be set from 3 kHz to 16 kHz. This setting will determine how often the drive sends the pulse groups to the motor. As the setting on the switching frequency is set higher, the resulting current waveform is tighter in resolution or "smoothed". However, carrier frequencies less than 3 kHz are audible (and unpleasant) to the human ear, therefore carrier frequency is commonly set within the 4 to 8 kHz range, and sometimes higher. At these frequencies the carrier

31

frequency closely approximates a pure sine wave. The more closely the current delivered to the motor resembles a pure sine wave, the cooler the motor will run.

- **Fundamental Frequency:**

This is the frequency of the voltage used to control the speed of the motor. Usually between 0 and 60 Hz, but can be set to go above the full-speed (60 Hz) rating of the motor. To create a fundamental frequency of 60 Hz current to a motor, with the carrier frequency set at the 4 kHz setting, the microprocessor would fire the IGBTs in such a way as to cause them to send 66 pulses of the DC bus voltage to the motor leads for every 60 Hz cycle. So the VFD would send 33 pulses for the positive alternation (half-cycle) and 33 for the negative alternation. Remember that the period for a 4 kHz frequency is .00025 seconds, and the period for our desired 60 Hz output is .01666 sec. Therefore:

.01666 / .00025 = 66.64 total per output cycle (60Hz)

33 pulses per half-cycle

At 8 kHz the number of pulses would double to 133, assuming a full-speed output frequency of 60 Hz is desired, creating a smoother current sine wave to the motor. Note that as carrier frequency is set higher, it can also produce voltage spikes that damage insulation on wiring and on the motor itself. This has become less of a problem if motors are wound with inverter rated wiring and also if distances between the VFD and motor are kept to within 100 ft. At longer distances, inductors or chokes are often used on the output of a drive to filter these voltage spikes and prevent damage to wiring and equipment.

Before moving on into the section of programming and troubleshooting, carefully study the following simple analysis of the PWM waveform. When using an oscilloscope to view output voltage, the pulse trace would of course be what is seen, as shown on the left side. Using current settings on the oscilloscope, the output sine wave can be viewed and is shown on the right. This is the resultant voltage/frequency output to the motor, and shown as the current sine wave that is superimposed over the pulse train.

Simple example of an AC induction blower motor (480 VAC / 3 ph) operating at approx half-speed (30Hz). Note that the number of pulses are determined by the switching frequency setting.

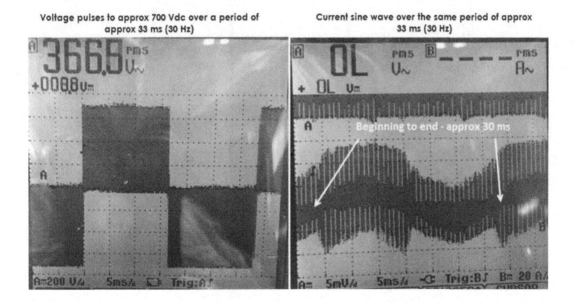

| Voltage pulses to approx 700 Vdc over a period of approx 33 ms (30 Hz) | Current sine wave over the same period of approx 33 ms (30 Hz) |

PWM sine-wave analysis!

Smaller pulse widths produce a lower output voltage at a "longer wavelength" resulting in a lower frequency. *V / Hz ratio remains constant!*

Wider pulse widths produce a higher output voltage at a "shorter wavelength" resulting in a higher frequency. *The V/Hz ratio remain constant!*

Pulse Width

Pulse Width

Current Waveform to Motor!

DC Bus Amplitude
Voltage for 480 VAC input:
480 x 1.414 = 650 Vdc

One Cycle

One Cycle

34

Control Modes - Speed and Torque Control:

We have discussed the general concept of maintaining a constant V/Hz ratio necessary for maintaining full torque throughout the speed range of an AC induction motor. Due to advancements in solid state technology there are now several methods of achieving this goal. Each one of these *control modes* offer different characteristics and benefits in terms of speed control and torque bandwidth, which is the optimum range of torque values a drive can provide given a specific frequency. The control mode, along with the different parameter settings, must be configured for each unique application. Many VFD's have the capability to provide control for permanent magnet motors, and are suitable for some types of positioning applications dependent upon the degree of accuracy needed.

- **Scalar control:**

Maintains a fixed V/Hz ratio over its operating range. Once established by the control set-up procedure the voltage supplied to the motor at various operating frequencies is determined and controlled by this ratio. This control scheme outputs both voltage and frequency in a linear fashion, generating 100% motor speed at approximately 480V and 60Hz. When the application calls for operating the motor at 50% of its rated speed, voltage and frequency would go to 240V and 30Hz. For a 460V/ 60Hz motor the ratio would be 7.67 and for a 230V/60Hz motor the ratio would be 3.83. These ratios are maintained unless *voltage boost* or *IR compensation* is activated, or if the frequency is increased beyond the level for which the system can maintain the proportional voltage. Ramp time adjustments are used to prevent acceleration and deceleration currents from exceeding safe limits. This method provides a torque bandwidth of approximately 10 to 50 Hz. A limitation of using scalar control is the fact of it being essentially an open-loop system. The VFD is outputting power to a motor without any feedback on the actual speed being produced. Modern VFD's often include custom macro and user-defined configurations having predetermined output curves that are non-linear or customizable. By using one of these configurations it is often possible to tailor the VFD/Motor combination for unique applications regarding torque and speed output. While *scalar control* is widely used for AC synchronous motors, it should be noted that it is not the recommended control method for permanent magnet (PM) motors.

- **Open-loop flux vector control**:

This type of control mode is also referred to as *sensor-less vector (SV)* control. It mathematically estimates speed to control the flux and torque producing currents in an AC induction motor. Vector drives dynamically regulate motor torque as directly and accurately as possible, by continuously monitoring and analyzing the motor current to determine what voltage to apply at any given frequency. The drive then uses this data to produce the *optimum magnetic flux* in the motor windings. It is referred to as *open-loop* because of the absence of any external speed or position devices, such as an encoder. Yet this type of control essentially functions as a *closed-loop operation* in that it *internally monitors motor current* and allows the VFD to quickly adapt to varying load conditions.

As compared to Scalar mode operation, the SV mode delivers higher starting torque, tighter speed control under varying loads, and can provide torque bandwidth of .6 to 300 hertz.

- **Closed-loop flux vector control**:

This control mode directly measures speed, usually by means of an encoder, to control the flux and torque producing currents to an AC induction motor. This type of control is often referred to as *vector control* and can provide a wide range of torque bandwidth from zero speed to 500 Hz. Vector drives, including the *open-loop* or *sensor-less* type can often provide more than 150% of the rated torque to smoothly accelerate high-inertia loads.

- **Direct torque control**:

A control mode in which the microprocessor uses two control loops – a *speed control feedback* such as an encoder, and also a *torque control feedback* loop. In this manner the processor is able to monitor both the actual speed and the torque load on the system, and performs inverter switching that will satisfy the calculated "error". This correction happens in microseconds making this a very efficient control mode for many applications. Speed accuracy for this type of control is in the range of 0.1 to 0.5 percent of the motor slip rating or the motor (nameplate rating).

This type of control, might be used on web-spooling equipment for composite materials, or other spooling equipment where tight control on tensions must be maintained, even as the diameter of material rolls are constantly changing.

CHAPTER 5: DRIVE INSTALLATION & PROGRAMMING

As with any type of electronics the best installations are those where equipment can be kept clean, dry and reasonably cool. Most VFD's have an operating temperature range of 0° – 40° C, or 32° to 104° F, and will also have a cooling fan integrated into the drive to provide airflow cooling over the heat sink. With any installation, ventilation and access for maintenance should be an important consideration.   It makes troubleshooting all the more difficult when test measurements or adjustments must be make in a poorly lit, difficult to access area. If your drive is rated and setup properly, in all likelihood it will not require much attention for many years, but best practices would mandate good accessibility. Some common issues with VFD drives may be the need to periodically clean filter media in control cabinets, replace cooling fans, and make minor programming or parameter changes. So, - when you install a drive – make it as maintenance friendly as possible.

Common Wiring Connections:

Aside from the main input power for the drive and the motor output terminals; a VFD will also employ a number of terminal connections used for control. These terminals and associated wiring will control different unique characteristics of the drive's operation. Many of these terminals are configurable by parameter options or provide auxiliary contacts that can be used as additional control elements for equipment. Drives usually have terminals for digital inputs that allow for 2-wire or 3-

wire control, start, stop, reset, forward and reverse, a run/enable and jog input, and also some digital inputs for preset speeds. While it is convenient to show 2 and 3 wire start/stop wiring with conventional pushbuttons, remember that these digital inputs can be (and often are) initiated from a programmable control platform such as a PLC or a CNC machine control processor.

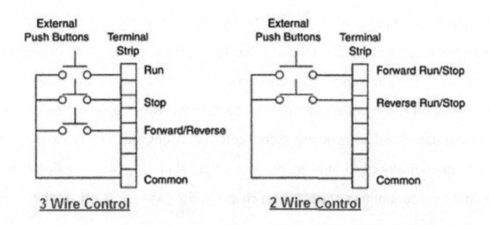

Normally drives will have the option of using an analog input, such as 0 to 10 vdc or 4 to 20 ma, to control its output. In many applications the control wiring for the drive is via Ethernet cable and networked from an OEM control platform such as a PLC. In these scenarios the only additional wiring that might be present in the drive is perhaps wiring for braking resisters.

Here is a diagram that shows some of the terminal connections that seem relatively common or typical to all drives. It is important to note that not all of the connections shown are necessary for the drive to run properly, and that many are dependent upon parameter setting.

Toshiba VF-S11

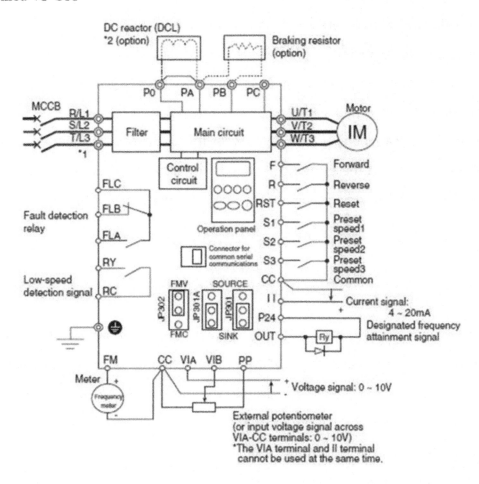

Usually the voltage at control terminals is derived from the drive itself, so no additional power beyond the incoming 3-phase voltage will be necessary. There are often *dry* contacts provided as well, which can be utilized by other control elements of the equipment. Speed adjustment will be accomplished by external potentiometer, 4-20 ma current signal, or perhaps by a 0-10 vdc analog input. These selections are normally set by parameter, but might also be set by a jumpers or dip switches found on the control board. If a pre-set speed is utilized from one of the digital inputs, note that the input is usually looking for either a "high" or "low" logic state, the actual speed/frequency associated with that input is a value that will be set by specific configuration parameters.

Fault detection contacts that are integral to the drive (see FLB above), will be used to shut down the drive and also other related equipment in the event of a drive fault or failure. CNC machinery, which often utilizes multiple drives for multi-axis machining, will usually connect these contacts in series or "daisy-chain" all the drives together in this fashion. If any single drive fails – the machine goes into an e-stop or fault condition.

Parameters & Programming:

Like any type of control platform, the configuration phase is one of the most important aspects of installing a VFD. It is accomplished by setting parameter values and perhaps the selection of certain "macro" programs included with the new drive. These macro programs can greatly speed up the setup process and are also selected by specific parameter settings.

Configuring drive parameters is usually accomplished by using the keypad display interface that is integral to the drive; however, in some models, a drive may utilize a "personality module" which must be programmed with a PC using the specific application software for the drive. In either case, programming is done by going through the parameter groups and setting desired values. Each parameter will specify a property that determines certain operational characteristics for the drive. These characteristics include such things as its operational *control mode, what type of speed reference will be used, motor data, gain values, switching frequency for the drive output, and acceleration and deceleration time values.* All of these details must be decided as you configure a drive to perform as needed.

Many manufacturers include hundreds of parameters that can be used. Even a relatively small drive will often have multiple pages of parameters listed in their manuals. While I usually scroll through every one when I setup a drive, I have also found that many times only a small portion of these, maybe 20 or so, are actually necessary. It should also be noted that drives are often shipped "pre-programmed" with default parameters. These generally are set to conservative and frequently used values that will pose the least risk to equipment and personnel.

Menu Navigation / LCD Programming Display:

On most programming displays, the software will be arranged in a menu-based system. Parameters will be assigned to specific groups and functional sub-categories. One group will define the general characteristics of the drive: *what language it will display? Time and date settings?* And determine *what will be shown on the display panel* once the drive is operational. Status items such as the frequency, voltage, or current are often displayed. Another parameter group will be the specific information about the motor being used – much of which will be taken from the motor nameplate. Other groups contain the information that determines exactly how the drive will operate, what frequency will it provide, what frequencies will be "skipped" over, what is the switching frequency desired, etc. One important aspect of the keypad/display unit is that it will usually allow the technician to bypass the remotely wired controls and to run the drive directly from the keypad (local mode). Also remember that on many types of drives; such as the ABB ACS-355 or the Altavar drives produced by Schneider Electric, program parameters can be saved or *backed-up* directly on the display programming unit, and written into internal drive memory. The display unit can then be removed, stored for safe-keeping, and used to restore a program to a new drive when necessary.

Common Parameters:

The following table lists 19 parameters that are commonly used and a brief description of each.

P#	Description	Default	Range
P-00	Remote Enable	OFF	ON / OFF
P-01	Acceleration Rate (sec)	5.0	0.5-30.0
P-02	Deceleration Rate (sec)	5.0	1.0-30.0
P-03	Minimum Speed (Hz)	5	3-30
P-04	Maximum Speed (Hz)	60	30-140
P-05	Current Limit (%)	150%	10%-150%
P-06	Manual Torque Boost (%)	2%	0%-10%
P-07	Volts/Hz Base Speed	60	30-240
P-08	RPM at Base Speed	1750	1-9999
P-09	Output Relay Enable	OFF	ON / OFF
P-10	Carrier Frequency (kHz)	8	4,6,8,12
P-11	Remote Reference Gain (%)	100%	60%-100%
P-12	Remote Reference Offset (%)	0%	0%-40%
P-13	Remote Reference Display Enable	OFF	ON / OFF
P-14	Electronic Thermal Overload (%)	100%	20%-100%
P-15	Thermal Overload Enable	OFF	ON / OFF
P-16	Coast Stop Enable	ON	ON / OFF
P-17	Reverse Disable	OFF	ON / OFF
P-18	Software Version	Read Only	N/A

Remote Enable: This setting will allow the drive's starting and stopping options to be controlled either in "local" mode via the drive keypad or in "remote" mode which would be from remotely located switches or control wiring.

Acceleration Rate: The "accel" time is the time period, usually in seconds, that the drive will take to accelerate to its full or programmed speed. This is basically a "soft-start" feature that limits inrush current to the motor and allows a smooth startup of load movement. A proper setting with this parameter will prevent "overcurrent faults" on the drive.

Deceleration Rate: The time period, usually in seconds, that the drive will take to decelerate the motor from full or programmed speed to a full stop. It is important to note that this setting is very dependent upon the load being driven. If it is a high inertia load with large mass then decel time must be adequate to stop the load. If too short a time period is set then "overvoltage" faults will occur on the drive, a DC bus fault, because of regenerated energy pumped back into the VFD. A braking resistor grid (dynamic braking) is often used to dissipate this energy.

Minimum Speed (Hz): A minimum frequency setting for output to the motor that is valid regardless of any other regulated speed setting from an external control.

Maximum Speed (Hz): A maximum frequency setting for output to the motor that is valid regardless of any other regulated speed setting from an external control.

Current Limit (%): This parameter allows the user to set the maximum percent of the drives current rating. This parameter setting will limit output torque and also the set accel and decel times to keep the drive within its current limit setting.

Manual Torque Boost (%): This parameter is sometimes referred to as "IR Comp". It is set as a percentage, and will provide additional voltage at very low starting speeds. This will cause the motor to provide extra torque during the startup of high inertia or high friction loads. This setting can cause "overcurrent" faults if set at too high a value.

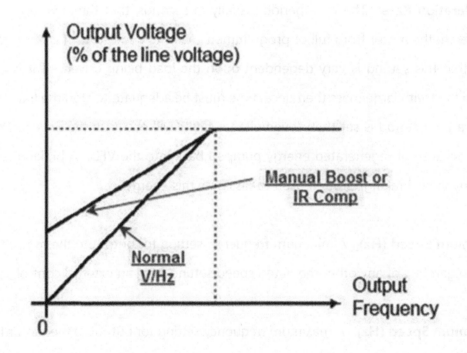

Volts/Hertz Base Speed: This parameter sets the base speed at the maximum output voltage and establishes the V/Hz ratio that the drive will follow through all speed or frequency ranges up to this maximum value.

RPM (Base Speed): This parameter scales the displayed RPM, if this option is used, to the base (nameplate rated) speed of the motor.

Output Relay (Configurable): This parameter selected how the integrated output relay is energized for the purpose of showing different drive conditions such as "running", "faulted", or "at speed".

Carrier Frequency (kHz): With this parameter the user can select the frequency with which pulses are sent to the motor output. In the above table the selections are 4, 6, 8 or 12 kHz but many drives are selectable to 16 kHz. Remember that lower carrier frequency settings, such as 2 kHz – 3 kHz, can cause the drive to produce audible noise which can be irritating. The higher the carrier frequency, the smoother the current signal will be to the motor and the smoother the motor will run. The downside of higher switching frequencies, is increased heating in the inverter section, and also the potential damage to motor and load cable insulation due to voltage spikes.

Remote Reference Gain (%): This parameter allows the user to scale the actual analog speed reference to a maximum other than the 10 vdc (if using 0-10vdc), or 20 ma (if using 4-20ma). For instance, if max speed needs to be referenced by 16ma rather than 20ma, then the Reference Gain would be set at 80%.

Remote Reference Offset (%): Similar to the Reference Gain, this parameter scales the minimum analog signal to the actual range of the reference signal. For instance if using a 4-20ma signal, the minimum would not be zero or 0 ma, it would be 4ma. Therefore the *Remote Reference Offset* would be 4/20 or 20%.

Remote Reference Display Enable: Allows the user to turn "on" or "off" the displayed speed.

Electronic Thermal Overload (%): This parameter selects the trip setting for the motor overload fault. Remember that the motor current rating may be less than the VFD current rating. Divide the motor current rating by the drive rating for the percentage setting.

Electronic Thermal Overload Enable: This parameter, if set to "ON", enables the thermal overload function and will protect the motor from overload to the value selected by the Electronic Thermal Overload (%).

Coast Stop Enable: If this parameter is enabled the IGBT's will simply turn off when given a stop command, which will then allow the motor to coast to a stop. Otherwise, if disabled, the IGBT's will continue to provide systematic firing to ramp the motor down and then turn off.

Reverse Disable: If set this parameter prevents the motor from being driven in reverse by the VFD.

Software Version: Usually a read-only parameter. It is important, when troubleshooting a drive, to have all the details, reference manuals, and also the software version before calling the manufacturer for technical assistance.

S-Curve Parameter: Not listed in the above table but often used to provide additional smoothing or "soft-start" and "soft-stop" capabilities. It makes adjustments to *not allow* a purely linear start or stop. This is a "time-based" parameter.

Critical Frequency or Skip Frequency: This parameter setting will allow the drive to "pass-over" certain fundamental frequencies that trigger mechanical resonance or harmful vibrations in equipment.

Automatic Restart: This parameter, for obvious safety reasons, usually has a default value of "OFF". It can, when the application allows, be set to "ON", where the drive will automatically restart if a non-critical fault condition has cleared.

Braking Methods:

These methods must be considered whenever installing or configuring a new adjustable speed drive to an existing application. During motor stops or when the load is overhauling, the motor will function as a generator turning mechanical energy in generated electrical energy.

The method you use will be dependent upon such factors as mass, inertia, and friction. Also a factor is the time it takes for a load to come to a complete stop. I have seen balancing equipment, used for jet turbine engine rebuilding, where a turbine or 1st stage fan section could take a long time to stop rotation. Only after these components came to a complete stop could balance corrections be made and retesting occur. So quite often, braking times directly affect production issues. These methods of stopping a load are set by VFD parameters but, as in the cases of *regenerative braking* or *dynamic braking*, may also require additional equipment and drive capabilities.

- Coast to a Stop
- S-Curve Stop
- Ramp to Stop
- DC injection Stop
- Dynamic Braking Stop
- Regenerative Braking Stop

Dynamic braking, and *regenerative braking*, are probably the most common methods used when loads must be quickly slowed to a stop. These methods dissipate the energy generated from the rotating equipment until the load comes to a stop.

Dynamic braking requires a resistor grid to dissipate the generated electrical energy that is forced back to the drive.

Regenerative braking utilizes forward and reverse IGBT bridges that are controlled by a microprocessor. The controlled firing of the IGBT dissipates the electrical energy generated by the rotating motor back onto the mains. It works well for applications that may require frequent stops. However, regenerative braking is typically a more costly alternative, although energy recovery savings can negate some of the initial hardware costs.

Flux braking: An additional form of braking, which many VFD's are capable of providing, is called *flux braking*. To implement flux braking, the drive must be configured for *direct torque control*. You may recall that this control mode has separate feedback for both speed and torque, and thus provides independent control for the flux-producing current and the torque-producing current supplied to the motor. Flux braking takes advantage of this separation to control motor braking. When the motor acts as a generator; during a stop and while overhauling, flux braking increases the flux-producing current in the motor. Rather than sending the extra energy to external resistors or back onto the AC mains, flux braking essentially uses the motor as the braking resistors. By increasing the magnetic flux in the motor, the load can be quickly decelerated. With flux braking, heat is dissipated inside the motor by the stator windings, so this method is best for applications that require less frequent stops. If the application requires continuous braking and frequent overhauling, other braking methods, such as *regenerative braking*, should be a better choice.

Here is a comparison chart for the relative stopping times using different forms of braking.

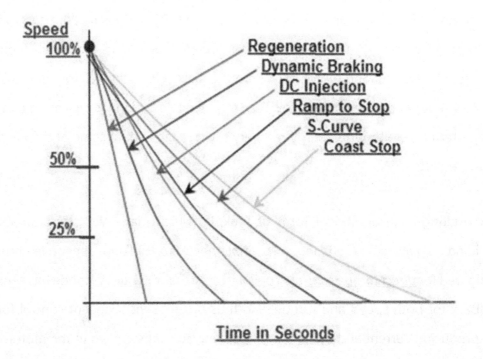

Once again, the method you choose will depend on the load, how quickly it must come to a complete stop, and also whether the costs of additional equipment, such as braking resistors or a drive with regenerative braking, is acceptable.

CHAPTER 6: TROUBLESHOOTING DRIVE PROBLEMS

There are many other areas of VFD utilization that might be discussed, including motor types, classes, and enclosures; formulas regarding power factor and harmonics, or detailed cost-analysis of using VFDs. These are topics that, while important, have not been the primary focus of this short book. Instead; I wanted to present a basic framework of concepts that might help those working as electrical service technicians, to more easily troubleshoot and resolve drive problems. Many technicians have experienced the tension and stress created when production equipment goes down due to some mysterious unknown, operators are idle, and production managers are asking *"how long will the equipment be down?"* This is the point where, as technicians, we need to be prepared to safely and quickly isolate problems with VFD driven equipment. What I attempt to present, are concepts necessary for troubleshooting most common VFD problems. The troubleshooting concepts presented here will – almost 100% of the time help you isolate and resolve a drive problem. To be effective in troubleshooting VFDs, or any other electrical problem for that matter, you must apply a systematic approach to troubleshooting.

Basic Troubleshooting:

As in all electrical problems, there are basic procedures to perform first when troubleshooting a VFD application. *Safety should always be your major consideration and the first step in good troubleshooting practices.* Be sure to install warning signs, place barriers around the test location to prevent pedestrian walk-thru traffic, and follow proper lock-out / tag-out procedures.

As is evident by now, VFDs are a complex combination of electrical power components and sensitive electronic circuits. They are controlled by feedback and microprocessor circuitry that can be very sensitive to induced voltages from other sources. With this said; it's important to remember, that correct VFD operation is dependent on many *external factors* such as the nature of the load, proper input voltages, power surges, proper cooling, ventilation and cleanliness.

Whenever troubleshooting a drive that has stopped functioning, it's a good practice to take as many test readings as possible with the VFD being in a de-energized state. I've occasionally seen instances where input fusing was blown and someone would simply put in new fuses and re-energize the drive. Of course, this is a dangerous practice and should be avoided until more thorough checks are made on the drive and motor. Another important test to make while in a de-energized state is a resistance and megger check on the motor, and also any cabling that feeds the motor. It's not uncommon for a bad motor to knock-out an amplifier or drive, especially in the case of servomotors.

Since many test measurements often must be made on energized equipment, it's important to remember that substantial AC and DC voltages are present within a VFD. Important readings to consider for energized testing are: the input voltage, output voltage, output current and frequency readings if possible, and perhaps the DC bus voltage. It can often be beneficial to use a scope when looking at DC bus voltage to verify good voltage levels, and that the DC bus is free of unwanted AC components.

In other words, are the diode-bridge and filtering capacitors working as they should? If this is not the case, then it's an indication of problems with capacitors or diodes within the converter / DC bus sections. This type of problem can be of particular importance when the converter supplies a common DC bus and several drive amplifiers, as is often the case with CNC machinery having multiple-axis positioning. As previously discussed, the voltage present on the DC bus can be at high and potentially dangerous levels. It will be equal to the peak voltages of the AC input, approximately 680 Vdc from a 480 Vac input, and this charge will be held by capacitors that are parallel across the bus. Therefore any voltage measurements should be taken with caution. Once the VFD is de-energized, a potentially lethal charge can be held for several minutes before dissipating - so always take a voltage reading on drive capacitors or DC bus before performing any hands-on work.

Once again, safety must be a priority when troubleshooting. Remember to follow state or local code requirements for performing any type of testing on energized circuits. Here in the United States it's the NEC and NFPA-70E guidelines, while Canada uses their own national code - the CEC, and most European countries follow the IEC. These documents provide guidance on working with energized equipment including PPE, protective clothing, and zone distances where barriers are required.

Asking good questions:

It has been said that troubleshooting skills are only as good as the questions we ask. Many times, it is relatively minor issues that bring production equipment to a halt, so it can be beneficial to at least consider basic things first. One of the most important questions of all; *what does the machine operator have to say?* They often give important details about the situation at hand. Possibly a fault occurred as they were making tension or speed adjustments? Perhaps they witnessed a jammed load or heard a loud noise from within an electrical control cabinet? All information that would more quickly point to a potential problem. Beyond this, there are many other questions to ask: Is the correct voltage present at the drive's input terminals? Are any breakers tripped or fuses blown? Is the drive receiving an enable signal? Is there a DC bus fuse that might be blown? What are the indications or fault codes shown on the drive display?

When these questions have been answered, it is usually possible to quickly narrow our focus to the actual problem issue. Included here is a list of common drive faults and some of the issues that cause them. These are often displayed on the drive display module, but it may still be necessary to have the manufacturer's manual with you. Some of these typical drive faults are:

Over temperature fault: This can occur if the cooling fans that circulate air over the heat-sink have stopped working, or if the heat-sink or the filters are clogged and dirty. On occasion the thermistor is simply bad or has a faulty connection.

Over-current fault: This fault may occur if the "overload" parameter is incorrectly set for the size of the motor, or if the rating of the drive is simply inadequate for the motor and load. Also remember that if extremely high carrier frequencies are used, the drive may need to be "de-rated", and be unable to produce the current necessary for the application. Other problems that could result in an over-current fault would be if a driven load became jammed in some way. Also note that if one phase of incoming power is lost to the drive it will continue to provide 3-phase output to the motor - but at substantial power loss.

Over-voltage fault: This fault can occur when incoming voltage to the drive is too high, so it is important to check and verify incoming power. Basically, this is a fault that concerns the DC bus voltage. If the incoming power is high, the bus will carry the approximate peak voltage of the incoming AC phases, and will be higher as well.

I have also encountered this general fault when a "deceleration" parameter being set at too short a time period, a heavy load is "overhauling" the drive, or the regenerative braking is not set properly. These faults can usually be reset from the keypad, or by a power cycle of the drive - but remember to look at *root causes* in these scenarios. As mentioned earlier, a good practice is to check the integrity of the motor connected to the drive. This can usually be accomplished with a DVM and a "megger". Megger or "ground-insulation" testing is usually done at the 500 Vdc or 1000 Vdc settings. As a general rule, a motor in relatively good condition will give a reading of 50 Megohms or greater to ground potential. Also, using a megger can test the integrity of the load wiring that feeds the motor. Any low readings can indicate the breakdown of insulation either in the motor or feeder wiring. Of course this is often caused by environmental conditions such as oil, coolants, moisture and dirt.

If motor and wiring checks are good (or within reasonable limits), you can remove motor leads and see if the drive will run without any load. If motor tests are good, then select the *local* option on the drive keypad and see if you can drive the motor. If so, then perhaps the problem resides in the control wiring "external" to the drive. Has the drive lost an analog speed reference or the enable/run signal that it requires to operate? If connected to a control platform, such as a PLC, are the wiring and cable terminations good, and is the VFD receiving the required output from the PLC?

If a drive is producing erratic speed control then the speed reference signal or feedback wiring may be acquiring background noise from other sources within a control cabinet. Is it shielded and grounded properly and are the connections good? Is feedback wiring routed near power wiring in the control cabinet? If so, this can be the cause of erratic movement due to unwanted noise on signal or feedback wiring. As these types of issues are checked and eliminated, it may eventually require some testing of internal components of the VFD. At the end of this section I've included a check-sheet that can be used to check many of these internal components in a systematic method.

VFD Internal Testing:

Often, drives do not have their own integral power supply but share a common AC source and a common DC power supply and bus. This can make it a bit easier to check the DC bus voltage since bus bars will often extend across the front of multiple drives. At the other end of the spectrum are the types of drives in which all the sections, *converter - DC bus & filtering - inverter* are all contained in one package. This type of drive, like any other electronic component, can be checked and verified, section by section and component by component if necessary. Usually, as in the examples below the DC bus will have terminals that are accessible and can be used for test purposes.

Note that some drives have very good "onboard" diagnostics which may tell you if a processor, base-driver firing board, or output transistor is at fault. It is usually necessary to consult the product maintenance manual for decoding the many "fault codes" that comprise these diagnostic aids. I recall a large spindle drive on a 5-axis milling machine that had a row of numbered test pins that could be checked for a high logic state. This row of test pins, depending on high and low states, provided the onboard diagnostics for interpreting, with the help of the manual, different problems within the drive. Fortunately, most VFDs today will use some form of digital display to present an alarm condition or fault code.

Next are some examples of DVM tests; I use a Fluke 87 meter and, for this example a Toshiba VF-S11 drive. Test points for input line (L1, L2, and L3), output (T1, T2, T3) and the DC bus (PA+, and PC-) are all brought to the front terminals which makes this drive easy to test. Please note that these diagrams show a power transistor with a protective diode on the inverter output side. As previously discussed, today it is much more common to find IGBTs *(Insulated Gate Bipolar Transistors)* in use. They have very fast switching times and use less current on the control side than a conventional power transistor, while providing for high current output. IGBTs are basically a hybrid between an IGFET and a normal power transistor.

Testing the Upper Diodes of the Converter Section

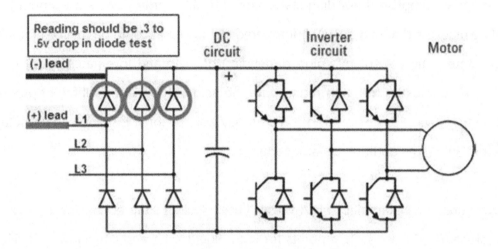

- Test each input terminal in this configuration; readings should measure a .3 vdc to .6 vdc voltage drop using the <u>diode check</u> selection on your meter. The difference depends on what type of solid state components, "germanium" or "silicon" and the "doping" procedure that turned their junctions into a "P-type" or "N-type" solid-state device. If your readings are open or shorted then the diode is bad.

- If this test is good, then reverse the leads – negative lead to the input terminal and positive meter lead to the DC+ bus, (PA+) in my example. You will probably see a brief charge-up of the capacitors but the meter reading should go to "OL" or read like an open showing no conductance. If readings are shorted then the diodes are bad.

- This same method can be used to test the *lower* diodes in the bridge and the results should be the same as on the other 3 diodes.

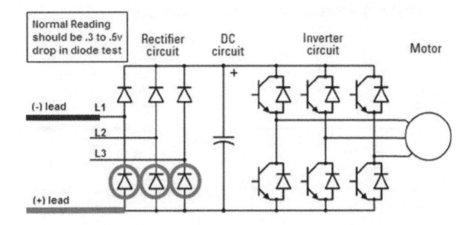

- At this point, it may be convenient to test the capacitors. One simple test is to put your meter leads across the bus terminals PA+ and PC-, while in the *diode-test mode*. You can see the caps charge to the voltage your meter can output, probably 6 vdc or so. As you switch the selector on the meter to read DC voltage you will read the charged voltage and see it slowly dissipate. Of course, a better test is made with an oscilloscope while the drive is energized to see if the voltage is steady and without dips or AC "ripple". Also it is a good idea to visually inspect capacitors for swelling, leakage and physical damage.

- Next we can test the output (inverter) section *protection* diodes. If these have failed then in all likelihood the transistor associated with that protective diode has also failed. Note that to check individual diodes, the motor should be disconnected from the drive.

Testing Protective Diodes in Inverter Section:

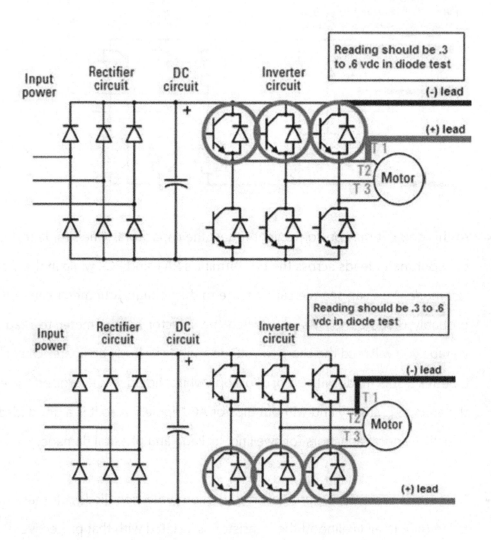

- Once again, note the placement of test leads and check for shorted or open diodes. The inverter transistors can be difficult to test because of requiring removal, but a quick check between output terminals, while in diode test mode, should show no conductance or "OL". Older style drives, having "Darlington pair" transistor packs, could more easily be tested, but I always found it convenient to have the "datasheet" handy when testing these units.

If these tests are good, then other potential problem areas may reside within the control and microprocessor areas, internal relays, or the internal switching power supplies of the VFD. These are areas where it may simply be more cost effective to purchase a new unit, depending on the size and HP of the drive. Many times a power supply can be acquired for replacement or repaired just like any of the other components in the drive package, but the cost in lost production may be the deciding factor.

Once again, these are *general* procedures for isolating a problem on a VFD. These same guidelines seem to work well regardless of the AC drive or its application. PWM drives are common in CNC machine tools with AC servo motors, and also a wide array of pumps, fans, lift tables, and conveyor systems. Included at the end of this section is a checklist that can be used as a reference when testing a drive.

VFD Internal Testing Checklist

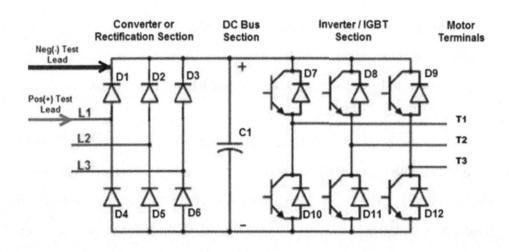

1. Measure Rectifier Forward Voltage Drop (diode test setting)

   Normal readings: .3 to .5 volts, Reversing test leads should read OL.

   - Red Lead to L1 / Blk Lead to + DC bus: D1 FVdrop _____
   - Red Lead to L2 / Blk Lead to + DC bus: D2 FVdrop _____
   - Red Lead to L3 / Blk Lead to + DC bus: D3FVdrop _____
   - Red Lead to – DC bus / Blk Lead to L1: D4FVdrop _____
   - Red Lead to – DC bus / Blk Lead to L2: D5FVdrop _____
   - Red Lead to – DC bus / Blk Lead to L3: D6FVdrop _____

2. IGBT Freewheel Diode Forward Voltage Drop (diode test setting)

   Normal readings .3 to .5 volts, Reversing test leads should read OL.

   - Red Lead T1 / Blk Lead to DC+ bus: D7FVdrop: _____
   - Red Lead T2 / Blk Lead to DC+ bus: D8FVdrop: _____
   - Red Lead T3 / Blk Lead to DC+ bus: D9FVdrop: _____
   - Red Lead DC$_{neg}$ bus / Blk Lead to T1: D10FVdrop _____
   - Red Lead DC$_{neg}$ bus / Blk Lead to T2: D11FVdrop: _____
   - Red Lead DC$_{neg}$ bus / Blk Lead to T3: D12FVdrop: _____

3. Bus Capacitor Series Resistance and Capacitance:

   - Ohm scale: Red Lead to (+) and Blk Lead to (-)   (if resistors are parallel across the Bus capacitors):
     _____ ohms

   - Capacitor test mode: Red Lead to (+) and Blk Lead to (-): _____ microfarads

   - Remove Capacitors and inspect for swelling, leakage, or other damage.

   - Test each individual capacitor for proper readings: _____ microfarads

4. Digital multi-meter (DMM) test procedure for IGBT modules:

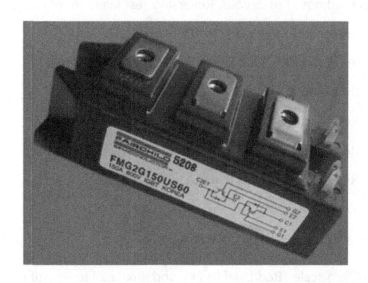

IGBT Diagram

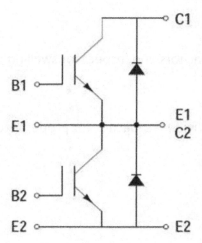

Collector – Emitter Junction Test

Note: (B1 & B2 may be labeled G1 and G2 on the IGBT)

1. Short out G1 to E1 and G2 to E2. With a DMM set to diode test mode, check across the C1 - C2E1 junction. With the (+) probe on C1 and the (-) probe on C2E1, you should see an open circuit. Switch the probes. You should see a diode drop on the meter.

2. Check across the C2E1-E2 junction. With the (+) probe on C2E1 and the (-) probe on E2, you should see an open circuit. Switch the probes. You should see a diode drop on the meter.

3. With a 9 volt battery, connect the (+) terminal to G1 and the (-) terminal to E1. Using your meter (set on diode test), you should now see a diode voltage drop across the C1-C2E1 junction in both directions now.

4. Connect the battery (+) to G2 and the (-) to E2. You should see a diode voltage drop across the C2E1 - E2 junction in both directions here as well.

5. If the IGBT passed all of the above tests, the IGBT is good.

Gate Test:

1. With the DMM set to test resistance, check between the gate to collector and gate to emitter. These should read infinite on a good device. A damaged device may be shorted or show leakage from gate to collector and/or emitter.

Summary

Many of the fault conditions I've encountered with drives have, in some way, been issues with the installation in terms of the configuration or environment. VFDs and drives tend to be quite reliable, and limiting factors tend to lean toward the issues of environment, frequency of preventive maintenance, and being sized appropriately for the application. Most of the time a drive will attempt to do exactly what we have configured or programmed it to do. If we accidentally program a maximum speed that is over and above the rated speed of the motor, set overcurrent limits incorrectly, or other important details improperly, the drive will attempt to run according to its programming – whether that will accommodate the load or not. While it's often tedious to read a manual, it really is important to be familiar with the drive you are installing, the application, and the programming procedures you'll use to configure the drive.

I hope this book has been helpful in developing a better understanding of VFDs and their usage in industry. As I've said before, I know you have many options when choosing books and online resources that discuss these topics; so I thank you for selecting my book. As always, I welcome your comments and feedback. My goal is to present relevant technical topics, and I have found feedback from my readers a valuable resource. If you would like to contact me with questions or comments you can do so at the following email address or by visiting my website:

ganderson61@cox.net

garyandersonbooks.com

OTHER BOOKS BY GARY ANDERSON

GARYANDERSONBOOKS.COM

PRACTICAL GUIDES FOR THE INDUSTRIAL TECHNICIAN:

MOTION CONTROL FOR CNC & ROBOTICS

VARIABLE FREQUENCY DRIVES – INSTALLATION & TROUBLESHOOTING

INDUSTRIAL NETWORK BASICS

RSLOGIX 500 PROGRAMMING SERIES:

BASICS CONCEPTS OF LADDER LOGIC PROGRAMMING

ADVANCED PROGRAMMING CONCEPTS

LADDER LOGIC DIAGNOSTICS & TROUBLESHOOTING

PID PROGRAMMING USING RS LOGIX 500

PROGRAM FLOW INSTRUCTIONS USING RS LOGIX 500

STUDIO 5000 LOGIX DESIGNER
A LEARNING GUIDE FOR CONTROLLOGIX BASICS

Made in the USA
Las Vegas, NV
15 September 2023

77499325R00044